NICOLA O'BYRNE

WHAT'S NEXT DOOR?

nosy crow

Hey!
Where are we?

I can't see a thing in here.

Can anybody hear me?

If you're out there,

clap your hands

to turn on the light!

Thank you. That's **much** better.
But who's this?

Hey! There'll be no **eating** in **this** book!
Let's help Carter get home,
but how can we **do** that?

I know!
Let's **draw** a door!
Crocodiles like water,
so use your finger to **trace**
the dotted line and
think very hard about
somewhere **wet.**

Well done!
That's a **brilliant** door!

And Carter's off!
But – oh dear – it looks
as if it's a bit of a **squeeze.**

Can you **jiggle** and **wiggle** the book
to help him through?

Crocodiles like water,
but this sea is **far** too **stormy**.
Poor Carter!

Quick!
Use **your** finger
again and **draw** a circle.
We need a drain before
Carter ends up as fish food!

Well, that's better, but Carter's soaked through. Can you **blow** on him to dry him **out?** That might cheer him **up** a bit.

Let's try again. We need somewhere less stormy.

Draw a door with
your finger and,
whatever you do,
don't think
of the ocean!

That's a **very good** door,
but crocodiles have rather **big bottoms**.

Can you **tip** the book to help him through?

Yep, it's definitely too hot!
Look, Carter's had to have a little lie down.

Quick! Fan him with your hand!

So, we need a place that's not dark,
not too stormy, not too cold
and not too hot.

We need to draw
another door!

Use your
finger to **trace**
the line and **think**
very hard about
somewhere that's
just right.

Great!

Off we go again!